DENTAL PRACTICE EXCELLENCE

3 STEPS TO AN ALL-STAR PRACTICE

DENTAL PRACTICE EXCELLENCE

3 STEPS TO AN ALL-STAR PRACTICE

ALEX NOTTINGHAM, J.D., M.B.A.

All-Star Dental Academy
1856 N. Nob Hill Road, Suite #175
Plantation, FL 33322

www.allstardentalacademy.com

Edited by Tom Wight

ISBN 9780997462500

DEDICATION

This book is dedicated to my wife, Heather Nottingham. She has always been by my side, taking my dreams and making them into reality. She is the best business and life partner! Thank you for not only giving life to our business, but also to our son, Zachary.

In association with:

THE DAWSON ACADEMY

As seen in:

dentaltown

Dentistry IQ

TESTIMONIALS

"All-Star Dental Academy® is a first-class operation. Their library of interviews and quality of the content they provide is excellent. **I challenge any dentist who is dead-serious about growing their practice to set aside time to listen to them.**"

– Dr. Bill Blatchford, DDS

"We are all progressing through the online training and continue to have regular staff meetings to learn and role play. All Star customer service has definitely become the culture of the office..... And IT WORKS! **The five-star reviews are rolling in and the phones are ringing off the hook!** In fact, I am making some new administrative and systemic changes to accommodate the growth."

– Dr. Jennifer Wayer, DMD

"We partnered with All-Star Dental Academy® because **they share our commitment to quality and service when providing top-notch training** in phone conversion and productive scheduling for dental teams."

– American Academy of Cosmetic Dentists

"We are excited to add All Star Dental Academy® to our Member Advantage Program. **Their online training programs are high quality** and can easily fit into a busy staff member's schedule."

– American Academy of Implant Dentists

"The Academy of General Dentistry has chosen All-Star Dental Academy® to join the AGD Exclusive Benefits program to help AGD members attract more quality patients through the power of customer service and training. **All-Star Dental Academy® is the only practice management training company selected to participate.**"

– Academy of General Dentistry

TESTIMONIALS

"I have nothing but praise for the program and the All-Star team. Due to their training, we have been able to grow from 188 new patients in 2015 to 377 in 2016. I can't wait to see what 2017 brings. Training my team with top-notch phone skills has definitely been a great investment! Thanks All-Star!

– Dr. Rick Rios, DDS

"I am so excited to have All-Star to help me get my team all on the same page, and to make the training and orientation of any new hires so much easier. All-Star has created a system that helps us provide the highest level of consistency and customer service to our patients. We feel great because **better, more consistent communication means more happy patients, better treatment acceptance, and more referrals.** I'm not in it alone anymore. I have an all star team to back me up every step of the way. Thank you, All-Star Dental Academy! I only wish you were here 20 years ago so I could've had your help from the very beginning of my practice."

– Dr. Sue Keller, DMD

"I've been a practice management and CE junkie since the start of my career and **I've never come across such valuable training for phone and communication skills.** I just wanted to tell you how much I am enjoying the training. I wish I had this resource 31 years ago when I started practicing and am excited that my son will have this knowledge from the start!"

– Dr. Peter March, DDS

"**My team is more productive and my patients are happier.** I highly recommend All-Star Dental Academy® as a fantastic resource in dentistry."

– Dr. Ron Richardson, DDS, FAGD
Former President of Florida Academy of Cosmetic Dentistry

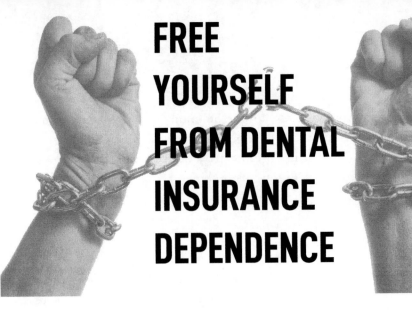

FREE YOURSELF FROM DENTAL INSURANCE DEPENDENCE

INSURANCE FREEDOM:
The 3 Steps to Taking Back Control of Your Practice

One reality of dentistry today is that by participating in dental insurance YOU MAY BE PAYING INSURANCE COMPANIES when you treat your patients.

In our no-cost webinar, discover the tools you need to break free of the stranglehold of insurance.

With the right approach, you can hold on to your patients, and free yourself of the burden of dental insurance.

- Learn the TRUE impact of dental insurance on your bottom line

- Why the state of dental insurance, inflation, and low reimbursements have made profitability a NIGHTMARE

- Why, because of write-offs, you are literally losing money with every patient visit

REGISTER NOW AT https://shorturl.at/oJMV4

"Working with our coach in the IF program, we dropped SEVEN plans, but retained well over 90% of our patients. We are making MORE MONEY, working LESS, and don't have to deal with all of those headaches from insurance companies. The impact has been HUGE. Everyone should do this program!"
- Dr. Cody Calderwood

CONTENTS

FOREWORD

I have a reputation of being a nice guy and somewhat soft spoken, but many of you don't know until you meet me that I'm very direct and honest. I don't like sugar coating. So, here is some straight talk.

Ask ten dentists what they think is the answer to unlocking profitability in their practice, and you'll get ten different answers.

But because I talk with dentists and industry experts daily about practice operations, I enjoy a unique perspective. The answer to the profit question is really quite simple: *customer service, phone training, and productive scheduling are the fastest and most effective ways to improve your dental practice's profitability.*

You work hard to get prospective patients to call your office, so why wouldn't you work just as hard to make sure each and every call has the chance to turn into an appointment? It's also crucial to ensure those appointments are scheduled correctly to get the most out of your practice.

What about marketing and automated systems?

I'm a big fan of marketing and systems. I've helped countless offices implement technology solutions that increase operational efficiencies and save money. I also speak around the world on dental marketing, SEO, web design, and email and reminder systems.

Any practice in today's economy has to market. Whether you need to at this moment or not, it is a good use of your money. Continually track and test different campaigns.

But, if you do not have a well-trained team, you are in big trouble. If you cannot convert phone calls into appointments and make sure patients show up, then you are throwing away all your marketing money. It blows my mind that dentists will spend many thousands per month on marketing without blinking an eye, or buy the newest and greatest technology (which you know I love), and will go to CE courses in exotic locations for themselves, but will not spend a dime to train their team.

Failing to train a team effectively is not only a poor reflection of a dentist's commitment to their staff, but it just doesn't make sense. You are missing out on significant revenue. Also, a happy and well-trained staff stays longer, which will make the experience you offer your patients even better and more profitable.

As for these automated reminder systems, while I'm a big fan, you must use them carefully. I see so many practices become reliant on them. The staff gets lazy or complacent because they think that the automated emails and text messages will make patients show up. But be absolutely certain - no technology can replace a human touch or caring voice. A strong connection between your practice and your patient is critical.

The fastest, most effective way to grow your practice is to invest in training your team, and not just any training. You need to master phone and customer service skills and the art of scheduling patients. You need to invest in a program that focuses on *service* and not sales.

There are many organizations that teach phone sales, or what my friends at All-Star Dental Academy call the "Get 'em in" approach. If you haven't learned to spot these folks (and stay away), this book will help you. A used-car sales approach is not a long-term recipe for success. I've seen too many dentists destroy their practice and team morale using programs like these. And be careful, as many of these companies may use the word *service*, but really only teach manipulative sales techniques. Do your research. See who the best in the business recommend. Read reviews. Ask around.

The rise of corporate dentistry and the continued strength of insurance companies makes the issue of training even more important, the private dentist has to find ways to compete. Corporate practices know the value of training. They do it. You need to train too!

I highly recommend All-Star Dental Academy for customer service, phone skills, and productive scheduling training. Hands down. Not only are they backed by the Academy of General Dentistry (AGD), the American Academy of Cosmetic Dentistry (AACD), and the Dawson Academy, but I have been endorsing All-Star since their inception. I'm proud to say that I am on their advisory committee and have contributed content to their educational courses. They are a humble group of people that really care about helping dental practices reach their full potential and making dentistry better.

I trust you will enjoy this book, which provides powerful insights into the All-Star philosophy and training.

Dr. Lorne Lavine, DMD
Founder and CEO, The Digital Dentist

INTRODUCTION

The typical dentist is diligent and hardworking, but at the end of the day, they often find little or nothing to show for all their effort.

This is the dilemma facing most dental practices: seemingly very busy, but not *productive*. The problem with being too busy and not productive is that it takes more time to accomplish an expected result. Therefore, sacrifices in other areas of life are required - whether that sacrifice is time with family, vacation, hobbies, or simply peace of mind.

This book is not about content, even though it is chock full of some of our best material. I've tried to take all the fluff out so we can get right to the point. I want you to be able to read something fairly fast without distractions and filler.

My goal is not for you to *enjoy* reading this book, although it won't be painful. My goal is that you **recognize areas of growth and take action** to build the type of business and life you desire.

Doctors have told me horror stories about working with training companies that were very disrespectful or rude. They would call the front desk teams (that they were trying to train) failures, and then turn to the dentist and say, "You get what you deserve." Those training companies love to contrast the challenges of the client with other successful dentists. I don't agree with this approach, and find it to be extremely counterproductive.

We believe that you DESERVE abundance. You are worthy of abundance. You just lack the tools and resources to get there. This book will be starting point for many, a reminder for some, and the catalyst for most to get moving, take action, and banish excuses!

Welcome to the next step on your journey to realizing your true potential.

The over-arching principles we're going to cover in this work are fundamental aspects of being *more productive* and *less busy*, so you ultimately have more free time and more money in your pocket.

It's always nice to hear about how well things are going. This is not this type of book. I don't sugar coat things.

I *will* be radically candid with you. What this means is that I'm going to be as direct as possible, but with love and empathy. Most communication I see is either indirect without empathy, which is manipulative, or direct without empathy, which is aggressive.

When we examine parts of life that are not going so well (or in this case, the dental practice), we are often presented with an opportunity to grow and get better.

But many dentists are satisfied with "good enough." What results do you think you get with just *good enough* effort? You may think you get good results. The reality, though, is that good enough effort only gets you **poor results**. Good enough is just the baseline – everyone is good enough. You have to be *good enough* just to be a dentist.

What about *great?* What results do you get when you strive for more and apply a more stringent standard? Typically, you'll only achieve *good* results. Are you starting to see a trend?

What about *excellence?* When you do an excellent job or commit to excellence as your standard, what results do you get? You get everything! You stand head and shoulders above your competition.

This book is about setting a standard of excellence, and how to *achieve it,* hence the book title, Dental Practice Excellence.

How do you get the most out of this book? Read it straight through. We've written it to be a quick and easy experience. You can mark it up with notes so you can return and quickly identify action items. If you can, read all in one session. I don't recommend that you skip around, as the content builds on itself.

If you want to become excellent in your dental practice and your life, read on…

CHAPTER 1

THE SILENT KILLER

Chapter 1: THE SILENT KILLER

There is silent killer threatening your dental practice profits.

When we think about dental practice losses, what comes to mind? Perhaps you spend too much on marketing? Typical practices spend thousands to tens of thousands per month on marketing. Or you might look to your supply company and say, "Well, I'm spending too much money there. That's what's causing me an issue with profits." Or maybe you point at your staff, "My payroll is too high, I can't afford them, and they're not performing appropriately."

These are just some of the internal factors you may question. Move on to external factors. What about competition? Seems like new practices are opening up everywhere. What about corporate dentistry? "Chain" dental offices are billing $7 billion at 10% of the market and are projected to grow to nearly 30% in the next three years. Perhaps it's insurance companies that are to blame? They are paying less and demanding more control over patient treatment choices.

Unfortunately, none of these issues is the root cause of the massive "bleeding" in your practice. They're not the silent killer that is sapping energy from the team and dollars from your wallet.

I'm not going to go keep you guessing. I'm going to tell you what the silent killer is, but you may not like what I'm about to say.

But first, I have to ask your permission to be completely honest and frank with you.

I believe it's my obligation that in this book that I tell you the truth. I'm confident that you don't want me to sugar coat anything or talk about topics that make you happy but you don't give you any results.

So here it is. The silent killer facing dental practices is *competency*.

What I mean by "competency" is that typical dentists and team members do not have the requisite business skills necessary to compete in today's marketplace.

"So are you saying we're all incompetent?" Well, yes, that's what I'm saying. Remember that I am going to be radically candid with you in this book. But it's not your fault. Dental schools don't teach fundamental business and customer service skills, and no one is born with an MBA.

Not too long ago, the average dentist could open a practice and patients would just show up. Maybe they just found you in the yellow pages. Dentistry was relatively a small community. Then we had insurance companies start to exert influence, and competition increased. Now, massive, well-organized, multi-office dental practices are gobbling up market share.

To compete effectively, the independent dentist must find a way to differentiate their practice.

As you will see in this book, failing to develop your business skills and implement them properly is resulting in massive losses in revenue and profit.

You may or may not be surprised that this is the number one issue facing the independent dentist. So why am I calling it a *silent killer?*

To help illustrate why this is a silent killer we at All-Star Dental Academy did a study with the American Academy of Cosmetic Dentistry and The Digital Dentist. The survey was sent out to over 40,000 dental professionals. About 85% of the sample were general dentists and the rest were specialists. We asked a simple question: *"How often does your dental practice train on business and customer service skills?"* The table below reflects our findings.

How often does your dental practice train on business and customer service skills?

Weekly	**1.5%**
Monthly	**1.5%**
Occasionally (less than once a month)	**47%**
Never train	**50%**

Our results reflect a dismal approach to improving fundamental business skills in the dental practice.

Basically, 97% of those polled either *never* train or train less than once a month. What is perplexing is that when I ask dentists face-to-face whether they should work on improving their business skills, they unanimously say they should.

Why is it that 97% of dentists fail to train themselves and their teams? Dentists aren't happy with the results they are getting with their current approach, but they're not going to do anything about it to improve the situation. I'm going to show you the impact of the silent killer on your bottom line. This should give you a sense of the massive opportunity you have to grow your practice by addressing some simple things about your practice. I'm going to show you how to overcome the silent killer.

In simple terms, three common signs and symptoms of the silent killer are: poor rate of new patient conversion; a negative hit to the bottom line from broken and changed appointments; and the pain from staff not performing as expected.

My promise to you is this: first, I'm going to give you the information, tools, and tactics to address these issues; second, at the end of this book, I'm going to give you a no-brainer offer on how All-Star Dental Academy can help rather than you having to figure it all out on your own. Plus, I have a special reward for those that read the entire book. If you read in order and diligently, you will find your gift.

The All-Star Story

So you might be asking yourself, "Who is this guy?" and "Why should I listen to him?" I am educated as an MBA and an attorney, so I share the value that all of you have in post-graduate education. I've worked as a business coach with companies from $1 million to $100 million. I was a top coach for Tony Robbins' business consulting group. I co-wrote a best-selling book with Brian Tracy on business success. I had the great honor of sharing the stage with Michael Gerber, the author of *E-Myth Revisited*, where we talked about the value of training and how to implement efficient systems. I've worked with hundreds of professionals and helped them improve their businesses.

My passion is breakthrough success done in the highest ethical manner. I believe great businesses can create significant personal wealth and make a huge positive impact on the people around us.

"I see you are proficient in business, but why dentistry?" you might ask.

I'll tell you with a story to help answer this question. My family are physicians and dentists, so I'm no stranger to the benefits and drawbacks of this lifestyle. But ever since I can remember, my father, who is a dentist, told me simply, "Don't be a dentist." My father had dreams of taking the best care of his patients possible, but insurance companies were beginning to influence the business of dentistry, and stood in his way. So I took my father's advice and instead of going into dentistry or medicine, I pursued business and law.

While I was still in law school, my father revealed that his practice was facing significant financial difficulty.

I offered to help. I implemented marketing systems and campaigns that drove a ton of new patient calls. However, the office was not converting the calls into patients. No matter how much we increased our marketing, new patient numbers were not going up.

I thought up what seemed like an oddball scheme. I approached my girlfriend at the time (who is now my wife), and asked if she would help. She had a background in high-end retail sales and customer service and she has worked for companies like Bloomingdale's, Kate Spade, and Theory as both a manager and trainer.

This gamble paid off.

She leveraged her experience, trained the staff, and helped them become more effective at converting new patient leads into patients.

We were able to double the practice by adding a million dollars in revenue in only 18 months.

Helping my father succeed and working with my girlfriend was an extremely rewarding experience. After my tenure with Tony Robbins, we decided to develop a training program to replicate the success we had with my father's practice. We would combine the best teachings from consultants and trainers with our experience working with dental and medical practices. And, thus, All-Star Dental Academy was born.

Today, All-Star Dental Academy is the leading serviced-based practice management training company with the most comprehensive online phone and scheduling training platform. We are business partners with the American Academy of Cosmetic Dentistry and The Digital Dentist, and have a formal "member benefits" relationship with the American Academy of Implant Dentistry. Most importantly, though, we are making a difference in the businesses and lives of our clients. You can see that in rave reviews from our dentists and team members.

So a little digression... Here's a picture of my wife and I. We're still very happy.

This is our son Zachary. He's got beautiful curls.

I had beautiful hair like that once, but it's gone. I hope that he keeps his curls and doesn't end up with a shiny head like me. And here's my son with our golden retriever puppy. They love to smash each other and have a good time. They're an adorable little couple.

Family is extremely important to me, and my father is my hero. He has done so much for me and I'm so grateful that I've had the opportunity to give back.

I've met and worked with hundreds of dentists and I see the vast majority of them share some common characteristics. They are caring, hard-working, and trusting people. So when I help a dentist I feel like I'm helping my dad.

Let's get back to business.

A little review: The silent killer we are talking about is *competency*. 97% of dentists fail to address the underlying issues. And the three signs and symptoms of the silent killer are:

- Poor rate of new patient conversion
- Drain on practice from broken and changed appointments, and
- Pain from staff inconsistency

My promise is that I will give you the information, tools, and tactics to make a significant positive impact on your business.

CHAPTER 2

**EXTERNAL FORCES
AND THE ALL-STAR
BUSINESS GROWTH FORMULA**

Chapter 2: EXTERNAL FORCES AND THE ALL-STAR BUSINESS GROWTH FORMULA

There is a reality in business, and life, where we are all constantly being affected by a myriad of outside influences. Every one of these influences is a force – either something's exerting influence on you and your business, or you are exerting influence on others – "No man is an island."

In a business venture, there is a constant struggle for balance between internal forces, which are things like motivation, and external forces. Until recently, you could just open up a dental practice and you'd be fine. Patients would come in, and you didn't have to worry – if you provided a decent level of care and provided an acceptable experience, achieving success was just a matter of time. But with the dental industry maturing, the requirements for success are getting more stringent. You really have to do a lot more than simply providing great dentistry. You have to run a great business and give your patients a great experience.

There are five main external forces that are exerting influence on the dental industry. They are:

- Insurance companies
- Corporate dentistry
- Marketing saturation

- Patient buying power, and
- Competition

We will discuss each in turn.

External Force #1: Dental Insurance

Dental insurance came on the scene in 1954. In the beginning, the concept was promising: Patients benefited from predictable premiums that enabled them receive the dental care they needed. Dental practices enjoyed robust compensation for the work they performed. And, of course, the insurance companies enjoyed decent profit margins.

Unfortunately, time passed and the hunger for profits drove "innovation" in the space. The result is that premiums increased, benefits failed to keep up with inflation, compensation for procedures were whittled away by 30 to 40%, and overhead for administrating plans in the practice reached outrageous levels.

Make note of two other important recent statistics: 60% of the population has some sort of dental insurance plan, and 74% of dentists accept at least one PPO.

The net affect on a dental practice is that you're going to be reimbursed less for performing the same procedures. Your net overhead will increase. You will be forced to find ways to cut costs to maintain margins. You may have to spend less time with patients to meet production goals. Ultimately, you're going to need more patients to get the same result – you're working more and getting paid less – the opposite of our goal.

This begs the question – *should you take insurance?* The answer, as with everything, is, "It depends."

The reality of the marketplace today is that competition is getting fiercer. If you're competing with other insurance-based dentists, what's going to entice one patient to choose you over another? And then there is the question of how to compete if you don't take insurance and your competition does.

The strategy for success, then, takes advantage of your ability to provide an exceptional experience through amazing customer service. Consider what you and your practice can provide to a prospective patient that will persuade them to choose you over your neighbor.

External Force #2: Corporate Dentistry

"Corporate dentistry," in case you have been living under a rock, is the trend of independent dentists choosing to sell their practice to a management group, or an organization opening practices like storefronts. Currently, corporate dentistry is somewhere between 3 to 5% of the industry. Some estimates suggest it's higher - nearly 10% or $7 billion. Predictions say that's its going to be somewhere between 20 to 25% of the industry before it plateaus.

It's easy to see why more than half of new dental graduates are joining corporate practices. It's a straightforward solution for the young dentist. They have to pay down student debt, which can be hundreds of thousands of dollars. There is little opportunity to open their own practice right away, and associate positions in independent practices are scarce. Joining a corporate practice is an easy choice because of the benefits they provide.

The point is not that corporate dentistry is good or bad.

What I want you to focus on is **what you can learn from them, and to develop strategies to be competitive.**

Consider that corporate practices are typically managed by experienced business people. Something you can learn from them is how to run your practice like a business. We'll explore how they operate and manage costs to maintain a healthy profit margin.

A huge advantage corporate practices have is in managing overhead. They have the experience and leverage to set up supply chains that can be significantly cheaper than what you can achieve. They come from Walmart and Amazon, and apply their skills to dentistry. As cost-cutters, they will win every time by taking advantage of those savings to slash what they charge for their services, and then make it up in volume.

You can't compete on price.

So, what *can* you do?

Instead, identify what makes you more appealing to a consumer. You CAN win on *relationship-focused service* that you provide your clients. THAT is what you can do better than any corporate practice; focus on relationships and service.

Ironically, corporate dentistry understands the power of service, and they work diligently to provide the highest level of service they can. Corporate dentistry has robust and formal training programs for staff. They recognize the value in investing in their people. This is in contrast to that poll we conducted with independent dentists that showed 97% don't train their staff AT ALL or only once a month. Why are most independent dentists failing to invest in training their staff? That's a very good question. We will explore this towards the end of the book. But ask yourself - Why are YOU not training your staff?

We know corporate dentistry trains. And we know the independent dentist does not. But you must realize that your front office team was not born with amazing customer service skills.

You can deflect the challenge by saying, "I'll just hire people who are already trained. Problem solved!" But how are you recruiting? Are all your recent hires superstars? Do you compensate better than corporate dentistry?

The bottom line is that the only way to compete with corporate dentistry is to play the game BETTER than they do.

Provide an *exceptional* experience so patients will choose you and your practice. This is key, because you are not operating under the pressure of meeting quotas – you don't push unnecessary procedures on your patients to pad your revenue numbers. But choosing to provide exceptional service requires a commitment to investing in your team.

The single most powerful advantage of the independent dentist is the concept of *self-determination*. YOU get to choose how pressure for bottom line results influences your decisions. You don't have shareholders breathing down your neck for quarter over quarter growth and more and more profits. You can choose to provide higher quality service because you are the master of your business. You choose where to invest time, energy and financial resources. You have more flexibility because you can choose what you want to do and how you want to do it.

Since you are not subject to the whim of a distant accountant, you can create a business strategy around building profitable, long-term relationships with your patients. If you can withstand self-imposed pressures and provide great service, in the long run, you will generate profit per patient that a corporate practice manager would drool over.

And there's no ceiling in terms of earning potential. It's your business; you can aim as high as you want. Associates in a corporate environment are limited by pay scale. But as an independent business, you are only limited by your determination and imagination.

External Force #3: Marketing Saturation

The third external factor is marketing. We find that independent dentists spend about 1.5% of their collections on marketing. Many practices spend 3 to 5% of their collections. That can be anywhere from $30,000 to over $100,000 dollars in marketing.

Those amounts are fine IF you are getting a decent return on that investment. The problem is that consumers are overwhelmed by marketing. Channels have become so cluttered and so competitive that you spend a lot more to get a lot less.

The solution to the challenge of effective marketing lies in being smarter and more efficient than your competitors. Carefully track results and test your marketing to make sure you're getting the best bang for your buck.

Choose a marketing partner carefully:

- Ask your colleagues what companies are working the best for them
- Look for dentists with strong online presence and see who they are using
- Make sure the company specializes in dentistry
- Ensure that you own your own website, rather than being beholden to someone else's proprietary software
- Check the company's references, and
- Avoid short, fast, cookie cutter proposals

External Force #4: Patient Buying Power

Inflation is a fundamental challenge for all businesses. Look at the cost of living in the 1940s. $3,900 dollars for a home? Today, that's ballooned by a hundred times, whereas incomes have increased only 40 times. There is a massive difference in terms of a comparison in cost of living and what a dollar will buy today.

That's inflation.

After adjusting for inflation, today's hourly wage has about the same purchasing power as it had in 1979.

This means that your patients have less money!

How does this affect you? You have to decide which consumers to target. You will most likely have the most success with focusing on the patients that understand the value of investing in their oral health, and the financial resources to act on that understanding.

Go back to your records and see if you see a trend in types of cases or demographics that you serve and that are the most profitable. You will see a pattern. Perhaps, you will even see the famous 80/20 rule, where 80% of your income comes from 20% of your patients. Find and target that 20% to get the most out of your marketing and time investment.

External Force #5: Competition

You have denser concentrations of dentists in prime population areas. You have regional and corporate practices with giant marketing budgets and experienced, professional support. Your competition is becoming more sophisticated when it comes to the business of dentistry. You have to be aware of this so you can compete.

More critical are *non-dental* competitive factors. As I mentioned before, patients with ever more limited resources have to make choices about what they want to use their money on.

Choices like a new house, car repairs, or a vacation. Do consumers want to get fillings, veneers, implants, root canals, or do they want to go to Disney World? Mickey's a lot more fun than veneers or a root canal.

The key is in educating your patients on the *value* of what you offer. The reality is that this is true for ANY business.

Give me any business model, any industry, any demographic, and I will point out someone that is doing amazingly well for themselves because of an emphasis on service and building up the value of what they offer. This is true for dentistry as well.

The All-Star Business Growth Formula

I want to show you how easy it is to grow your business with a proven business growth methodology.

The fundamental component of the growth formula is training. We've discussed the power of investing in training, and below, we will dive into the specifics of why training is so critical, and tied so closely with generating revenue.

Opportunity for growth begins *before* the results of training are felt. It begins with some mechanism to drive leads to your practice, such as marketing efforts, or leveraging the insurance plans you accept.

Training comes into action by effectively converting leads into patient appointments, and then ensuring the patient shows up, accepts treatment, and refers. We will discuss the details of call conversion in Chapter 3, and setting up the patient to honor an appointment in Chapter 4. But for now, you need to accept that this is fundamentally how a dental practice generates revenue. It's that simple.

When you maximize the impact of a highly trained staff, your reliance on marketing and insurance can be lessened. You can minimize the impact of external factors.

Our assumptions:

- Your team converts 35% of phone calls into appointments
- 85% of patients show up
- 60% of patients accept treatment
- 15% of patients refer, and
- Revenue goal is $1 million

Let's see how this plays out. We'll use rounded numbers for ease of explanation.

To generate a million dollars in revenue, you need five million in opportunities. Here's how it works. Out of five million in opportunities, only 35% convert, so you are looking at $1.75 million. Of that, only 85% show up, which drops us to $1.5 million. Only 60% accept treatment, so your revenue is reduced to $900,000. But, 15% refer, which bumps us back up to our $1,000,000 revenue target. You need five million at the start to finish with a million when you go through this process. See the graphic of the process on the next page.

$5 Million in OPPORTUNITIES

Phone Conversion ▶ **35%**

$5M * .35 = **$1.75 Million**

Show Up ▶ **85%**

$1.75 M * .85 = $1.5 Million

Case Acceptance ▶ **60%**

$1.5M * .60 = $900 Thousand

Referral Rate ▶ **+15%**

$900K * 1.15 = **$1 Million**

What would happen if we just improved just a little bit, say a 5% net improvement, in each part of that process?

Let's keep our beginning number for opportunities at $5 million, and see what happens with an incremental improvement. Five million in opportunities, and an improvement in conversion from 35% to 40% gets us to $2 million. Instead of an 85% show up rate, it improves to 90%. That gets us to $1.8 million. 65% accept treatment, which takes us to $1.2 million. And finally, 20% refer, giving us a bump to $1.4 million.

$5 Million in OPPORTUNITIES

IMPROVE by 5% over baseline

Phone Conversion ▶ **40%**

$5M * .4 = **$2 Million**

Show Up ▶ **90%**

$2M * .9 = $1.8 Million

Case Acceptance ▶ **65%**

$1.8M * .65 = $1.2 Million

Referral Rate ▶ **+20%**

$1.2 M * 1.20 = **$1.4 Million**

We added $400,000 in revenue by just incrementally improving conversion, acceptance, show up rate, and referrals. 5% improvement is relatively easy. Now what if we want to be bold? What if we target a 12% improvement in each step? Let's see what happens.

Start with the same $5 million in opportunities, with a 47% conversion, not 35%. This gives us $2.4 million. 97% show up, $2.3 million. 72% accept treatment, $1.6 million. And 26% refer, rewarding us with $2 million.

$5 Million in OPPORTUNITIES

IMPROVE by 12% over baseline

Phone Conversion ▶ **47%**

$5 M * .47 = **$2.4 Million**

Show Up ▶ **97%**

$2.4 M * .97 = $2.3 Million

Case Acceptance ▶ **72%**

$2.3 M * .72 = $1.6 Million

Referral Rate ▶ **+26%**

$1.6 M * 1.26 = **$2 Million**

You just doubled your business by improving in each of these areas 12%, a relatively modest change.

The take-away here is that training your staff to make incremental improvements in phone conversion and getting your patients to show up results in a MASSIVE impact on your bottom line.

That's why you are here. You can potentially reduce your marketing budget, get more out of what you are spending, have the freedom to take insurance or not, and you're ultimately more productive.

CHAPTER 3

POOR CALL CONVERSION

Chapter 3: POOR CALL CONVERSION

Let's get started. The first symptom of the silent killer is poor call conversion.

Why is call conversion important? First, it directly affects revenue. Consider that when a prospect calls, they have acknowledged a need, researched your office, found your phone number, and made the time to call. They are primed to do business with you.

The average dental practice receives 135 new patient opportunities per month. But only 48 of those opportunities convert to appointments. That's only a 35% conversion rate. Basically, two-thirds of calls into the practice are not booking appointments. That's 87 appointments not booked. And, according to the American Dental Association, the first year value of a new patient averages $642.

If the typical dental office is open four days per week, we have 16 working days per month. For simplicity, let's assume only ONE missed conversion opportunity per day. From those statistics above, you can see that typically it is much, much more than one per day. But for our calculations, we'll just say one per day. That's 16 missed opportunities per month, at the ADA's $642 per new patient. Add it up and you are losing out on over $10,000 in missed revenue per month.

16 days per month	1 MISSED conversion/day	$642 ADA average revenue per client	$10,000 lost revenue per month

And if you look long-term at the lifetime value of a new patient, with the lifetime calculated at 10 years, that's approximately $100,000 that you just lost over the next 10 years from ONE month of failing to convert just that ONE call per day.

The second reason call conversion is important is that to make up for lost opportunities, you're going to have to work harder. You're going to spend more money on marketing and be in the office for more hours. So you're working harder - not smarter.

Finally, missed call conversion opportunities are a drain on energy. You have to keep trying to fix the same problems again, again, and again. Not only are you losing money but you're losing energy. You are not focused on what you do best – dentistry. You're going home saying, "What did I accomplish? I was busy but I wasn't productive."

The solution to poor call conversion is a system of training that empowers your front office team to increase their effectiveness. All-Star Dental Academy teaches a patient-centric, service-based system of call conversion called the GREAT Call™ Process, designed by our phone skills instructor and VP of Training, Heather Nottingham. "Heather is a million-dollar customer-service genius," Vicki McManus, CEO of The Productive Dentist Academy.

GREAT is an acronym. It stands for Greeting, Rapport, Engage, Ask for the appointment, and Take information.

One key aspect to any effective call conversion process is that it is specifically designed to be effective. That means it has to be followed very closely. Call conversions are like a puzzle, or a combination lock. You can do all the elements in the GREAT Call™ Process, similar to entering numbers on the combination lock, but you must have them in the right order for them to be effective. Jumble them up and the lock won't open.

Let's start with the **GREETING**

The Greeting begins with the salutation, what you say when you first pick up a call. The most important thing is that it sounds natural, friendly, and is consistent.

Part of the Greeting is to get the patient's name and welcome them to the office. Further, ask for a contact number, and how they found the office.

Note that asking for the caller's name and using it in conversation is an extremely powerful way to establish a connection with another person – probably the most effective way to connect. In a study done by Call Tracker ROI, only 1% of employees will ask the caller for their name during the conversation. So 99% of employees are not getting the name of the client. This is crazy. Keep this statistic in mind; I will bring up again about how important it is to get and use the caller's name.

Establishing **RAPPORT**

The next step in the GREAT Call™ Process is building Rapport. What is "rapport?" Basically, it is making a meaningful connection with someone. For our purposes, building rapport is the easiest way to have your practice stand out from the crowd.

However, in a "traditional" sales process, rapport is basically ignored. It's that insignificant amount of time you spend being "friendly" before moving on to focus on closing (in dentistry, "closing" means getting the caller to make an appointment). This approach reflects a "Get 'em in!" philosophy and is the prevailing approach that I see being taught to dentists and their teams by some consultants and "training companies."

The Traditional Sales Pyramid "Get 'em In!"

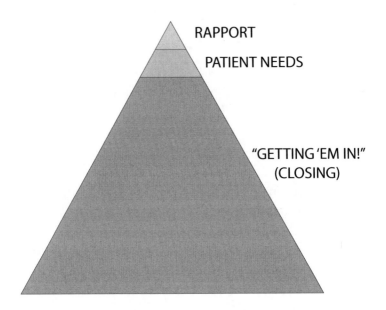

The "Get 'em in!" approach teaches that your only goal is to get the patient to make an appointment, at any cost. This means you don't answer questions, don't try to overcome objections, and deflect any and all concerns on the part of the caller in favor of getting them into the office. This approach is manipulative and it can go as far as to be unethical.

If callers have a question about insurance, for instance, the typical technique is to just answer, "I'm sure we can work with your insurance. Come on in and we'll deal with it when you get here."

This approach is so very WRONG, because what happens is the caller comes in, they have the wrong expectations about the appointment, they get angry about feeling mislead, they leave displeased with the experience, go home and write a blog, tweet, Facebook post, Yelp, etc. about what a bad experience they had in your office, and tell everyone they know to avoid your practice. Ouch.

In contrast to the "Get 'em in!" approach, we teach a patient-centered, customer-service based style of engaging a caller. We flip the traditional pyramid on its head. Our pyramid is called the VIP Pyramid (Very Important Patient Pyramid).

The V.I.P (Very Important Patient) Pyramid

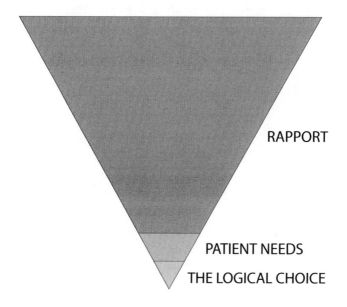

RAPPORT

PATIENT NEEDS

THE LOGICAL CHOICE

The vast majority of your effort with the caller is spent on building rapport. If you are successful at creating a connection with the caller, you can easily transition to understanding the caller's needs. If you can meet those needs, the caller senses that you are the logical and emotional choice to serve them, and they make an appointment.

Here are some important things to keep in mind about rapport:

- Use the name of the caller in the conversation
- Paraphrase, and repeat back to them what they said
- Ask positive, open-ended questions versus closed questions (yes or no questions are bad for conversation and rapport)
- Be an active listener, and
- Be engaged in the conversation

There's a great book by Dale Carnegie, *How To Win Friends & Influence People*, (perhaps you have heard of it?) and he said, "Remember that a person's name is to that person the sweetest and most important sound in any language." Bottom line, use the caller's name! And, as I showed you earlier, only 1% of front office teams take advantage of this powerful rapport-building tool. This is an easy 1% club to join.

More GREAT Call™ tips:

Don't...

- Interrupt
- Talk about what you want to talk about
- Make patients repeat themselves
- Talk about things off-topic
- Type while talking to the caller (use pencil and paper)
- Try to hold multiple conversations
- This last one, unfortunately, happens so often... don't be rude to a patient. If you're going to be rude to a patient you're in the wrong field

One very interesting and useful technique for building rapport is called "mirroring and matching." This technique comes from the research done by Dr. Milton Erickson, a psychiatrist and psychotherapist. A patient would come in to see him very agitated and would say something like, "Oh, the world's not so good and this and that. I'm upset with this person and that person," and then Dr. Erickson would say – using the exact same tone and emotion – "Oh, I know how you feel and it's really understandable. Why don't you sit down and we'll talk about that?" And his patient would later report feeling, "Wow, this Dr. is a lot like me. I like him."

Fundamentally, rapport is all about "likeability" and making a connection with someone. And if you're similar to someone, if you can mirror him or her, match their demeanor, and connect from a genuine and engaged place, there's nothing else as powerful.

Building rapport appears to be simple, but it takes a lot of talent. There is a wonderful quote by Stephen Covey, "Seek first to understand, then to be understood." In other words, strive to be compassionate and empathetic to get yourself in the mind and heart of the person you're working with, and then help them understand you and how you can help. This is the bottom line of what we teach. Get into the caller's world and understand them, and then bring them into your world by guiding them to an appointment that is just right for them.

I'm just covering the tip of the iceberg on building rapport. I know that the dental practice is a very busy place, and there's so much to be done. Sometimes we might think, "But I'm good with people," and that that is enough to be successful on the phone. But there's tons of research on rapport, and tons of techniques. You can always get better at it. So a big part of our training program is teaching rapport-building theory and techniques and encouraging everyone answering the phone to practice.

Getting down to business with **ENGAGE**

The next stage in the GREAT Call™ Process is Engage. Engage involves answering the caller's specific questions and overcoming objections. This stage allows you to position your practice as the best choice to meet the caller's needs.

In almost every call, you will have to answer some common questions such as, "What do you charge for veneers? What do you charge for an implant or orthodontic services?" You will also have to answer specific questions about the caller's needs, such as "Why do I need x-rays, I just want a cleaning."

You'll also want to be prepared to overcome "objections," which are arguments that the caller may try to use to justify NOT coming to your office. I know it sounds odd, but it's very common for someone, even when they know they need dental work, to be reluctant in making an appointment. And it is not just your office they don't want to visit; they would rather not make ANY appointments. So you have to be prepared to gently and respectfully negate their arguments. Common ones you'll hear are things like: "Oh, that's too expensive," or, "I can't afford that," or, "Your office is too far."

Another component of Engage is to position your practice as the best choice to meet the caller's needs. We call this "Sharing the Sizzle." You want to highlight how your office is different and special and how you are ready to provide the caller the best care possible. Key sizzle points usually involve anything special about the dentist – training, skills, areas of expertise, etc. – and the office. For example, highlight unique features and emphasize the calm and pleasant environment, even go so far as to call it a "spa-like experience" if you offer such a thing.

Remember that for the best results with the GREAT Call™ Process you have to follow the order of the steps. Often, front office teams will engage in a shorthand version they have picked up over the years – an acronym we call "EAGR."

What happens is, as it sounds, the staff will engage a caller immediately at the start of the call. The caller may ask, "What do you charge for veneers?" The team member will instantly answer, "Oh, we charge $2,000." They engaged with the caller without having any kind of connection - they haven't built rapport, they haven't even greeted the patient or asked their name! Most often, the staff will then move directly to asking if the caller would like to make an appointment. Typically, at this point, the call is lost. The caller doesn't make an appointment, but rather just says "Thanks," and moves on to the next phone number, hoping to call an office that makes them feel welcomed and valued. Sound familiar?

ASK for the appointment

After answering questions, overcoming any objections, and sharing the sizzle about your practice, it is time to actually ASK the caller to make an appointment. It is appropriate at this point in the process. If your team has built rapport with the caller, it will be a simple matter of finding a spot in the schedule that works best for the patient and practice.

There are some things to consider in this stage, though. There is specific verbiage and an order to the appointment process. Does your practice say, "When would you like to make an appointment?" Or worse, "Do you want to make an appointment?" Can you see the challenge here? Any time you give the caller an opportunity to say "NO," they will. So consider using instead this verbiage: *"Let's go ahead and get you scheduled."* Follow this up with, "Do you prefer mornings or afternoons?" It's proactive and assertive, without being pushy, and gently guides the caller into a "Yes."

Another important part of the appointment process is to set expectations for the appointment, create some urgency, and get a commitment from your new patient that they will honor the appointment time. I could write a chapter on each on of these elements. They are so very important!

If you fail to do any of these things, your new patient will come in confused and angry, or they just won't show up. This process is covered in much more detail in the (full) training program.

Get the details – **TAKE INFORMATION**

The last stage of the GREAT Call™ Process is to Take Information needed to properly prepare for the patient's visit. The biggest mistake that is commonly made is to try and take too much information too early in the call, or not being thorough enough at the end of the call.

Asking for information too early, without having established rapport, doesn't get you anywhere. Likewise, rushing at the end of the call and missing important details doesn't set your practice or the patient up for a successful appointment.

All-Star Role Play: What Do You Charge For…?

I want to share a role play with you. At All-Star Dental Academy we have 20+ role plays with the transcripts available. Please note that a role play and transcript like what I am presenting here is not a "script" to be used by your team. Scripts are TERRIBLE for building rapport, as you will inevitably sound like a robot, or a person reading. That's not how human interaction works! Use these transcripts and role play as a guide to help understand the underlying process and concepts involved.

All-Star Dental Academy Phone Success Course, Module 9, Unit 8: Role Play Transcript - "What do you charge for veneers?"

Heather: Thank you for calling the office of Dr. Awesome, this is Heather, how may I help you?

Alex: Hi Heather. I wanted to find out what you guys charge for veneers?

Heather: I'd be happy to help you with that. First, can I get some information so I can better assist you?

> *This is a transition statement, which means we are breaking the state of the caller, who is fixed on price. We ask if we can "better assist." Nearly everyone loves to be assisted better. Now, we can ask questions and take control of the call so we can more effectively help the caller.*

Alex: Yes. What do you need to know?

Heather: First, who do I have the pleasure of speaking with?

> *Get the callers name! You should know by now how important a person's name is, right?*

Alex: My name is Alex.

Heather: Hi Alex. Can I ask when we last saw you in the office?

> *Repeating the name is a good idea. Heather is also assuming caller is a current patient because you want to avoid mistaking a current patient for a new patient. It makes them feel more welcome.*

Alex: I am not a patient… I've never been there before.

Heather: Ok, wonderful Alex! Welcome! Can I get a contact phone number, just in case we get disconnected?

> *Getting a contact phone number is critical so you can call back if you get disconnected, and also implies consent to follow up with them. Otherwise, using caller id, you can seem like you are stalking them.*

Alex: Ok, it's 555-4444.

Heather: Let me repeat that back to you. You said 555-4444, correct?

Alex: Yes, that's correct

Heather: Great...and who can we thank for referring you?

> *We assume that the caller was a referral. The caller will correct us, but we planted a seed in their head that we get lots of referrals.*

Alex: Um, I just did a quick Google search and your office came up.

Heather: Ok, super! So Alex, when you initially called you were asking about veneers. First, are the veneers for you or someone else?

> *Beginning to build rapport.*

Alex: They would be for me.

Heather: Fantastic! Now tell me a little bit about your dental situation. What made you think about getting veneers?

> *Heather is using positive, open-ended questions to build a connection.*

Alex: Well, I have always been unhappy about the color of my teeth. They are kind of yellowed and I have tried whitening many times but it really doesn't make a difference.

Heather: I see. So you are looking to get a really nice white smile.

This is an example of paraphrasing and repeating.

Alex: Yes

Heather: And approximately how many teeth were you thinking about doing?

Now we are going with more focuses questions. Remember, we started with open-ended questions.

Alex: Probably around eight upper teeth.

Heather: Ok, that's great. Now Alex, have you seen any other cosmetic dentists to discuss your interest in the veneers?

Alex: Not yet. I just started calling around to different offices to get prices.

Heather: I see. So a dentist didn't tell you if you are a candidate?

Alex: No, not yet. I think I should be since the only thing really wrong with my teeth is that they are discolored.

Heather: Well the best way for us to help you and see if you are a candidate is to have you come into the office and meet with Dr. Awesome. Now, you initially asked about the price of veneers. In order to give you a specific price, we would need for the dentist to evaluate you in a free consultation we offer. I can give you a basic range so you at least have an idea of our pricing. Does that sound good?

> *Heather is beginning to use "Show and Tell," which will build value and put the price in context. Now, we are in the ENGAGE section of the GREAT Call™.*

Alex: Yeah, I don't need an exact price... I just want to see if it's feasible or not for me.

Heather: I completely understand. Now, I want to first give you a little background info about how we come up with the price range. There are three elements that go into the price of veneers and our other porcelain restorations. Those three things are 1) the skills and training of the dentist, 2) the quality of the lab we use, and 3) the customer service of the staff and office experience. Those three things will vastly set our office apart from most other practices in the area. And with dentistry you will find that it is true - you get what you pay for. I can tell you that Dr. Awesome has been in practice for 35 years, he is an Accredited Member of the American Academy of Awesome Dentistry, and only 500 dentists exist with that training in the US! And patients travel from all over the world to see him. We use the best lab in the US and they only work with the top 2% of dentists in the country. Finally, we are proud to offer an amazing, spa-like experience when you visit us. Our veneers range from $1,295-1,595 per tooth. The final price will be based on how many teeth you have done, which lab you choose, and how complex your case is. Those are all things you will be discussing with Dr. Awesome in your appointment. How does that sound?

> *Notice how Heather "showed" the value and how her practice determined the fees. Then, she Shared the Sizzle, highlighting what makes her office special. Finally, she provides a price range.*

Alex: Sounds good to me.

Heather: Fantastic! Let's go ahead and get you scheduled...

Heather *asked* for the caller to make an appointment, and the patient scheduled. Most likely, he will be very excited to come in. To conclude the call, Heather will *take information* and set the appointment up properly, so there are no misunderstandings.

Even if she did not schedule the appointment, I guarantee you that this patient had a great experience. We often see that patients who don't schedule immediately (on the first call) will call back when they go down the street and see the huge difference in customer service they receive.

Remember, when you are engaging in customer service, you are planting seeds that will sprout in a big way, but you must be patient.

***

You will see three significant benefits of employing the GREAT Call™ Process. First, you're going to have more high quality patients that make appointments. Second, those patients are going to accept treatment. And finally, they are going to refer their friends and family

When properly executed, your patients will show up for their appointments. When you set appropriate expectations, and help the patient understand the value of an appointment, they will think, "Wow, I'm in the hands of a professional!" Compared to everybody else, you stand out. Remember that incremental improvement from the business growth formula? Ultimately, through building rapport with your patients, they will show up and are set up to accept treatment. All the elements we talked about earlier.

I want to take a moment and answer some common questions we get about phone conversion training.

"Isn't it more important to get patients off the phone fast?"

I've heard this and people have said, "Oh, avoid verbal vomit," suggesting that you should have an arbitrary time limit, such as two minutes. In almost every case, this is a bad idea.

Look at the great Fortune 500 companies that are know for amazing customer service. They will simply stay on the phone as long as needed to take care of you. I understand that the typical dental practice doesn't have a call center or seemingly endless resources to devote to incoming calls, but you should begin to consider the time spent with a new patient lead as an investment, not a waste.

However, reality shows us that you must also consider the law of diminishing returns. If, after you've gone through the GREAT Call™ Process, addressed their needs, built rapport, and it's still going back and forth, then politely say, "Let me follow up with you. I'm here if you need any more questions answered." But it is critical to treat patients like people, not numbers.

"Can we just figure out the insurance and other stuff when they come in for their appointment rather then getting into it on the phone?

I often hear about practices that really buy into the "Get 'em in" strategy of call conversion. They'll say, "Oh, don't worry about insurance. Let's get your appointment booked and we'll figure out your insurance then." But guess what happens? The patient comes in and it ends up you don't take their insurance. At a minimum, they experience disappointment and anxiety about suddenly being asked to pay a LOT more than they anticipated (never ever a good way to approach financial matters). Some folks promote offering something like, "Oh, we'll comp you the exam," because you don't take the insurance. Stop manipulating people. Nobody likes the bait and switch. This approach It may result in an appointment, but long-term it's going to kill your brand.

"Do you use scripts?"

Do we use or promote using scripts? No. We use transcripts as a teaching tool, but never promote the idea of their use on a real call. We have verbiage and processes. The major problem with scripts is that you will almost always sound like you are reading something, and your callers will pick up on that. It sounds horrible. Instead, you have to go beyond scripts. Scripts might be good as a crutch to help you here and there, but you have to go to the next level. You have to train and practice typical scenarios and verbiage until responses are natural.

"Isn't building rapport easy and natural, or just common sense?"

Well, if it was, everyone would be doing it correctly. But really, it's not easy. It takes practice. We have 20+ role plays and transcripts and verbiage sheets and all this to help you with training. Bottom line is that if you train in the GREAT Call™ Process, you will be more successful at understanding the elements and the techniques will becomes part of you. That's what's going to help you be successful at call conversion using rapport.

Our friends have some nice things to say

One of our dentists is Dr. Ron Richardson. He recently said this, "As a practicing dentist and former president of the Florida Academy of Cosmetic Dentistry, I am no stranger to training programs. I understand the significant benefits that a consistent approach to customer service and scheduling training brings to a practice. It's hard work, but the payoff is phenomenal. My team is more productive and my patients are happier. I highly recommend All-Star Dental Academy as a fantastic resource in dentistry."

The most interesting thing about Dr. Richardson's story is that he had tried other programs before utilizing All-Star Dental Academy. He used one sales program that helped his front office increase the number of new patients, but he got cancellations through the roof and ended up losing money. And I've heard this happen countless times. It's upsetting.

I want to caution you about getting caught up in the "new patient syndrome." The important thing is NOT how many patients you get each month, but how many patients show up, accept treatment recommendations, pay their bill on time, and refer.

One of our practices had 117 new patients one month and then they had 50 new patients the next. The first month (117 new patients) was their worst in years in net profit. And the 50-new-patient-month was one of their best. They did well over $200,000 in production. So it's not how many patients but the quality of the patients coming into the practice that matters most.

CHAPTER 4

BROKEN APPOINTMENTS

Chapter 4: BROKEN AND CHANGED APPOINTMENTS

The next symptom of the silent killer is broken and changed appointments. Why is this important?

First, and most directly, it's a loss of revenue. According to Dental Economics, the average hourly production of a doctor is about $500 an hour, while a hygienist produces about $100 an hour.

If the doctor has two broken appointments per week, $500 an hour adds up to $4,000 per month. That's assuming each appointment was only one hour of work. If it was a more involved case the losses can add up pretty quickly.

Unfortunately, I have worked with doctors that have suffered entire day's appointments no-showing or rescheduling. Their whole day is crushed. That's thousands of dollars in production - gone.

Add in lost revenue from hygiene appointments. A hygienist with eight broken appointments per week, at $100 an hour, adds up to $3,200 per month.

Combine the two and you are looking at a very conservative $7,200 lost per month, or $86,400 per year.

I asked two doctors who recently joined All-Star Dental Academy to add up their broken appointments. Keep in mind, these practices were about $2 million in production. The two practices ranged from $250,000 and $300,000 in broken appointment costs. Wow! There is tremendous growth potential in fixing just this one issue.

The more subtle danger from broken and changed appointments is that you are then required to work harder to make up for those losses.

A Dentistry IQ analysis demonstrates that if you can increase production of the doctor by $50 an hour, you are looking at an additional $73,000 per year per hour in production gained. Those broken appointments cut right into that average production. If you have a lot of broken appointments, your average hourly production goes way down.

It's also a drain on energy. Our head instructor, Larry Guzzardo says this, "There's nothing that makes my blood boil more than broken and changed appointments. It's enough running a dental practice, and then to have money stolen right out of your pocket."

Now there are many reasons broken appointments occur, but fundamentally, it is a problem in perceived value. The patients that don't honor appointments don't understand how much your time is worth, so they don't have any qualms about breaking an appointment. Many times, though, this is not the patient's fault. Have you ever heard your front office team say, "That's ok, when would you like to reschedule?" Probably too many times to feel comfortable about it.

But there is hope! Your patients CAN be taught to value their appointments. And RIGHT NOW is the best time to start. As Hall of Fame basketball coach John Wooden has said, "If you don't have time to do it right, when will you have time to do it over?"

The solution to broken appointments lies in All-Star's Triple "S" Scheduling System. It consists of three parts. First is the Setup, you want to make sure that you are scheduling productively. That has to do with pre-blocking and other issues that are beyond the scope of this book. The second step is you want to make sure they Show up. That's what we'll be discussing here. The final step is that you must take care in promoting Subsequent appointments.

Making sure they show up

Before you can expect your patients to show up and be on time, doctors, *you've got to show up!*

It's incredibly frustrating for patients to wait, and wait, and wait for their appointment. You need to be on time, schedule productively, and not rush. If you are late, apologize to the patient. Let them know that their time is just as valuable as yours.

Now that I scolded you a little, let's talk about *patients* that aren't showing up.

First of all, we have to acknowledge that there's a difference between *broken* and *changed* appointments. A broken appointment is where you're getting less than 48 hours notice. A changed appointment is when you do have more than 48 hours notice. While we work with patients on the phone in the same way to set up an appointment, there is a difference in how to handle broken and changed appointments.

Dealing with broken appointments is not unusual in other businesses. Think about the airlines. If you're late, you miss your flight, period. Sometimes the airline will be generous and apply fares to another flight, but the consumer has a basic understanding that if they miss the flight, they are out of luck. You know people value their flights, so why is dentistry any different? Unfortunately, *patients are usually taught that it's perfectly acceptable to break or change dental appointments.*

Is this your office? Front office team member to a patient on the phone: "Thanks for letting us know. *When would you like to reschedule?*" or, "Ok, *would you like to reschedule?*" or, "Call us back *when you're ready to reschedule.*" Do you see the problem? With those responses, the staff is TRAINING the patient to casually break or reschedule appointments.

And the problem is compounded if the front office team gets annoyed with a patient and threatens a penalty or fee. Chances are the patient will not pay it, they won't return, and they'll tell their friends how rude you are, and maybe post a negative review online. Yikes. The whole situation happened because you were trying to be nice, the patient took advantage, you got mad and then retaliated. An unfortunate situation, but very typical of how many practices operate.

Avoiding the cost of broken and changed appointments begins even before your patient makes an appointment. First, you have to make sure that you teach patients the *value* of their appointment. This will almost guarantee they'll keep it. How do you build value for the appointment? Remember the GREAT Call™ Process? There are a number of critical steps in the process that contribute to establishing the value of the appointment.

Build Rapport. Very simply, patients are much, much less likely to break an appointment if they feel like they are important to you and when they have a connection with you. Consider who, in everyday life, you are more likely to skip lunch with – an old friend, or someone you've never met? The improvement in patients keeping appointments is really worth the extra five or ten minutes your team spends on the phone. Other programs may teach "Two minutes and then get off the phone..." Can you imagine how many appointments get broken with this approach?

Answer questions, overcome objections, and share the sizzle. It seems very simple, but if you don't take the time to get to know the needs of your prospective new patient, you are setting yourself, and the patient, up for disappointment. Make sure they end the call without any doubt that your practice is the right one for them, including things like the proposed treatment fits their budget, and that you work with their insurance plan. That just makes sense, right? If you were shopping for a pickup truck, you wouldn't call a dealer, have a conversation, make an appointment to drop by to take a look at their stock, only to be disappointed and angered by the fact that they only sell bicycles. What would you tell your friends about that experience?

Also, share some of the great things about you and your practice. This is an obvious way to bolster the perception of value in the patient's mind. Highlight specialized training and awards, the friendly staff and the great atmosphere in the office. Don't be obnoxious, but don't be shy in talking up why they will love you.

Set expectations. An important part of the appointment process, after you have found a date and time that works for everyone, is setting appropriate expectations for the patient. It's so powerful to go into a new situation with as much information about how things will go. It really helps keep people feeling comfortable, and the more at ease we are with the idea of something in our near future, the more likely we are to follow through on the plan.

Create a sense of scarcity. Robert B. Cialdini, PH.D., spent a career investigating the psychology of persuasion, and identified six of the most powerful motivators in getting people to do what you would like them to do – and doing so with integrity.

This last point is important, because you should never use these techniques to manipulate patients into coming into your practice.

But I'll assume that since you are reading this book and not others, you take great pride in conducting yourself in a professional manner. Note that the motivators Cialdini researched are inherent to human behavior so you have to be careful that they are not abused. They are all "buttons" that get pushed, and people naturally react in a predictable way.

One of the motivators that Cialdini identified that is very appropriate to our discussion of broken appointments is creating a sense of scarcity in the mind of the patient. Typically, if people know there is an abundance of something, they are less inclined to act immediately to get some for themselves. We are comfortable with the idea that what we want will be there when we want it. How does that apply to appointments? If a patient thinks that they can break an appointment because they can reschedule for the next convenient time, there isn't a lot to dissuade them from doing just that. However, if they have the expectation that appointments are scarce, then they will be more likely to keep that appointment. There is specific verbiage, techniques, and training for the front office team that support this, and we will talk about that in a moment.

Get a commitment. This one simple thing may be the most important technique for ensuring a new patient shows up. Adding the phrase, "Will you make me a promise to keep your appointment or call us at least 48 hours ahead of time if you can't?" to the conversation greatly improves the chances that patient will show up. It's another technique that leverages basic human behavior – the desire to keep one's word.

Can you see a common thread? I won't make you guess – it's that the GREAT Call™ Process was designed to make a **massive im-**

provement in the number of appointments that are kept. And recall, the most important thing about new patients really isn't simply the number of appointments you book, but the number of new patients THAT SHOW UP!

Dealing with broken and changed appointments

What can we do to work at reducing or eliminating *changed appointments?* Remember that a changed appointment is when you have appropriate notice (at least 48 hours), but it's still a problem.

Here is some verbiage that the front office team can employ when someone calls in to reschedule an appointment. But before we begin with the verbiage, there are two things you must understand to keep all of this in context:

#1 – Verbiage: We share verbiage, not scripts. The difference is that with scripting you need to follow it exactly as written. The downside to this is that you tend to sound like you are reading from a script, and it's hard to be flexible with a caller. Whereas with verbiage, you are free (and encouraged) to change the wording to fit your office, demographic, and what makes you feel comfortable. Verbiage is a starting point. Once you make it your own, you move towards mastery.

#2 – Tonality: I'm sure you heard the old adage, "It is not what you say, but how you say it." When you are using the verbiage we provide, you may think at first that it seems harsh or too strong. I recommend that you never just read it like a script, but practice and work on changing your voice to soften the language or adjust the wording to soften. The objective of what we are teaching is NOT to punish the patient or be mean, but rather to convey that appointment is valuable and that the patient should carefully consider the impact before canceling an appointment. So, practice and roleplay with your team until you can get the verbiage and tonality just right. Not too nice and not too strict.

Respond to the request to change an appointment with, "Oh! I'm sorry to hear you would like to change your appointment. We were looking forward to seeing you. What's going on?"

The question at the end, *"What's going on?"* is a way to both show compassion and identify silly excuses. If it is a silly reason, you can highlight it and contrast with the importance of honoring the appointment and getting the necessary work done for their health.

A note on excuses. Patients are notorious for excuses. The fact that they forgot, or were too busy, or found something more fun to do, is not an acceptable reason to miss an appointment. Sometimes you'll get, "Oh, but you did not confirm the appointment." The patient can get away with this if you have a policy of calling to confirm and they don't get the message (or say they didn't get the message).

This is part of the reason we don't believe in confirmation calls. Instead, we take the approach that the appointment is confirmed *when it is made.* Even go so far as to use that language when you are entering the appointment. Say near the end of the conversation, "Great, it is confirmed! We will see you on the date and time of the appointment." If you plan on calling, at least label it a "courtesy call." Ultimately, when it comes to reasons patients try to reschedule or cancel, you will have to come with some standard as to what is and is not an acceptable excuse.

Assuming the reason is legit, you can begin a teachable moment. You can say, "Let me see when our next available opening is," which triggers a process.

Look at the schedule and then offer the patient a time four to six weeks away. You begin to reinforce the concept of scarcity by reflecting a full schedule. Make sure to convey that you're concerned the patient could not come, that the team member and the doctor were excited to see them, and then give them another opportunity to honor the original appointment.

"Are you sure you don't just want to have your appointment already booked?" Chances are they'll keep the appointment. They don't want to wait four to six weeks.

We treat *broken appointments* a bit differently.

Let's take a look at the first incidence of a broken appointment with an individual patient. Begin dealing with the initial broken appointment in a similar way to the changed appointment: "We were excited to see you," etc.

An important difference is that you need to emphasize the significance of breaking the appointment. Give them a "warning shot." The warning shot works in this way, "Perhaps I never told you or maybe you forget, but we typically charge for broken appointments. I'll make an exception this time, but I'll need to note this on your chart."

You see, instead of penalizing them, and making them upset, you're seen as generous. Remember to use a disappointed tone to communicate empathy and the feeling that the doctor was looking forward to seeing them. Suggest that the only dates for rescheduling are six weeks out. It is important to note the broken appointment in the chart.

Now if a specific patient has a second broken appointment here is a suggestion on how to work with them. Express disappointment again and add, "When appointments are not kept affects so many other patients waiting for treatment. It also really hurts the practice. It will be practically impossible to find a patient to come in on such short notice."

It's important to evaluate the value of reappointing this patient. Chances are that if a patient has broken two appointments, they will break a third, fourth, and so on. If the patient insists on a new appointment, consider asking for a deposit. If they don't want to give you a deposit well, obviously you see their level of commitment. Alternatively, you can not set a new appointment, but rather suggest that they call in on a day that they would like to come in to see if there are any openings in that day's schedule.

Developing a policy for broken and changed appointments

Here are a few thoughts about a policy for working with broken appointments.

First, create a policy that encourages the team to take a positive approach, so they *teach* rather than *punish*.

Second, a solid policy should reflect the concepts of the GREAT Call™ Process, which will help more patients show up, and set them up for a positive experience, ultimately leading to greater case acceptance.

Third, as we've mentioned, a solid policy will help the office be more productive and less busy because you don't have to work harder to make up for the holes in the schedule.

Remember the true costs of those holes: two broken appointments with the doctor per week, at $500 an hour adds up to $4,000 per month. Eight broken appointments for hygiene, at $100 an hour adds up to $3,200. Save yourself $7,200 a month by putting a policy in place and supporting it with the training the front office needs to implement it.

I want to take a moment and address some common questions about broken and changed appointments.

"Should we charge for broken appointments?"

No. As I mentioned, the patient is not likely to pay and it's going to make them mad. It's reasonable to ask for a deposit to hold a reserved time for their next appointment, but don't force the issue.

"How do we keep the schedule full and enforce the policy at the same time?"

Setting the patient up correctly via the GREAT Call™ Process and then enforcing a positive policy teaches patients to keep their appointments and thereby reduced the overall broken appointments in the future. So just put together the policy, put it in place, and train the team in the GREAT Call™ Process and how to work with broken and changed appointments.

"How can the entire team, including the doctor, help reduce broken appointments?"

This is a good question. The reality of the situation is that the entire team does contribute to the overall patient experience, and helps the patient understand the value of their appointment and the care they are receiving.

Additionally, good documentation of broken and changed appointments, and the reasons provided by the patient, helps the clinical staff to understand behavior patterns. It allows the clinical staff to mention to the patient when they show up for the next appointment, "I noticed that you had to cancel your appointment a couple of times before you got here today. Suzie says you *[repeat reason for missed appointment]*. I hope everything's okay." When the patient realizes that the clinical staff is involved, including the doctor, they may make a change in their behavior.

CHAPTER 5

STAFF INCONSISTENCY

Chapter 5: STAFF INCONSISTENCY

The third symptom of the silent killer in your practice is that your staff may not be performing to the level you need. Your people are what really makes or breaks your practice. The most skilled clinician in the universe can't run a practice by him or herself. You must rely on the skills, energy, and dedication of your team to have a successful business.

Poor performance by your staff typically leads to one of three scenarios:

First, the staff member may ultimately leave their position, as most people don't like doing a job that they're not really good at. Also, consider that they may be underperforming because their boss (you) is not providing them the support are/or resources they need to be successful.

Second, the dentist or owner may let the team member go because of poor performance.

Lastly, the dentist may keep an underperforming employee on staff due to the trouble of replacing that team member.

If a staff member leaves or is let go, it's called "turnover." It's a reality of life and business that people come and go, but it is certainly not fun, nor cheap. Turnover takes a significant toll on your bottom line.

A study by Bent Erickson & Associates and Graddsaff.org showed that turnover costs will typically be one to three times the value of the employee (or what you pay the employee). You have hard recruitment and interview costs, costs of investment in training a new employee, loss of production during the switch over and training, drops in efficiency, increases in overtime for other staff, and make-up costs. It adds up surprisingly quickly.

Let's look at a rough calculation of replacing a staff member. We'll use 1x cost of salary to replace, where an average front office employee is paid $30,000. That means, at a minimum, it's going to end up costing you $30,000 for a turnover event.

A Harris Interactive Poll showed that poor training opportunities contribute to an increased likelihood that a new hire leaves by three times. You can imagine that it starts getting expensive when you have a lot of turnover.

Another thing to consider is that turnover has a significant impact on staff morale. A Gallup Organization study reflected that there are 22 million *disengaged* employees. A disengaged employee is one that is no longer interested in doing a job to the best of their ability. They are going through the motions, as it were. 22 million employees is approximately 20% of the U.S. workforce, ultimately costing the economy as much as $350 billion a year. So if you have a staff of five, most likely you have a disengaged employee. You can see how morale has a huge impact on the bottom line of a business.

Additionally, having staff not perform is stressful. According to the American Dental Association, *"An overwhelming majority of dentists report staff-related issues as the number one stressor in their practices."*

Think about how most practices train. They do this by trial by fire. They throw the employee in and hope that they figure it out. And then we wonder why dentistry has a super high turnover rate. Most training is haphazard, inconsistent, and unpleasant. Gains made from typical training tend to fade over time, and doesn't help with retaining employees.

The solution is to train like the Fortune 500.

You've probably read a ton of books about running a dental practice, maybe watched a bunch of "training" DVDs, or even attended seminars. But what typically happens when you are done? Does anything change when the team is back from that weekend seminar?

Probably not.

Maybe everyone is excited for a day, or maybe even a week, but the enthusiasm fades.

You might say, "Well, knowledge is power, right?" Wrong.

Knowledge is only *potential power*.

In his book *Think & Grow Rich*, Napoleon Hill goes into great detail about how knowledge is only potential power. The way to generate real power is to learn how to take that knowledge and implement it, put it into action.

As I mentioned earlier I had the great pleasure of sharing the stage with Michael Gerber, author of *The E Myth Revisited*, where we worked to promote putting effective systems into place, how to effectively train your employees, and how small businesses can model the best of the Fortune 500.

Let's jump right into it.

The first step in training is *onboarding*. Onboarding is designed to make new hires feel welcome and ensure that they're prepared for their new position. It gives them confidence and the ability to contribute and it does it quickly, typically in 90 days or less. Also, there's accountability for results.

If you take The Ritz Carlton for example, their onboarding program is 90 days long and they won't allow a new employee to touch the phone until the end of their training. Contrast that with most dental offices, where you get somebody new into the practice and day one they're answering the phone. If you have someone ineffective on the phone, how much will it cost you in missed opportunities?

Do you recall the impact on revenue with just one missed conversion opportunity a day? In all likelihood, these misses are happening hourly. And without proper training, your team is not likely to be doing everything possible to avoid broken appointments, so those are probably too high as well. But this level of performance is not their fault. *You're not giving them the skills and support to succeed.*

According to a study by Wynhurst Group, a formal onboarding program improves employee retention by 58%, and with continual training opportunities to improve skills, employees are likely to have a three-year plus tenure.

According to a CareerBuilder report, 60% of employees feel that skills will be learned on the job, while nearly 50% feel that the responsibility for training is equally shared between employers and employee.

The next stage is comprehensive, on-going training. This is where you build your competitive advantage. Remember that poll we did? 97% of dentists don't train regularly. However, this is a tremendous opportunity for YOU. If you are training consistently your team, you're ahead of 97% of your competitors. If you accept that comprehensive training leads to better skills, and better skills directly relate to improved conversion and fewer broken appointments, you can begin to see the advantage you will have in the marketplace.

What does it mean to "train" your team? It's our opinion that while consultants and seminars can be powerful tools, the value and effectiveness diminishes rapidly over time. Most of these training seminars try to pack in too much information, folks get overloaded, and never put their learnings into action. And consultants are fantastic when they are in the office, but they typically are "in and out," leaving a practice with a list of action items, but no mechanism for oversight.

Modern training takes a very different approach. The Internet has proved to be an amazing platform for engaging and effective training programs. Some estimates suggest that over 60% of training is now online, and that number is predicted to continue growing. A training program also needs to be systematic and progressive. Scattered and disjointed programming is ineffective at encouraging lasting improvement. Study units should be manageable in size, as the typical training period is less than an hour. Anything much longer than that and retention suffers. Study plans and/or action guides help trainees along the way. And finally, there should be a feedback mechanism to ensure retention of knowledge, such as quizzes or exams.

What about the question of *when* to train? Every organization is going to find their best methodology, but most dental practices have at least a half-day during the week for administrative tasks. This is a perfect time to set aside a half-hour for a training session. Supplement the weekly half-hour sessions with check-ins at huddles, or review progress in weekly team meetings. You might ask your staff to train at home (especially easy when you are using an online program that allows 24/7 access). Check your state law with respect to out of office training, and I suggest you compensate for the staff's time.

We have found that the best method is for team members to work at their pace on an individual basis, and then come together as a team to review, practice, and explore how to effectively implement learnings into the daily routine. It's typically less effective when training is relegated to a once a month binge. Retention and application suffers. It may work for college students fuelled by caffeine and anxiety, but it doesn't apply well to the real world.

Do it little by little, every week, come together, test, practice, and implement. Very simple. It's not a sprint, it's a marathon. Just 20 minutes per week is all you need.

Here are a few more thoughts on feedback mechanisms. Quizzes, and exams are self-explanatory, and can be part of a certification process to ensure retention. Regarding the issue of phone call conversion, nothing beats reviewing and evaluating real, live (or recorded) calls handled by your staff.

Now everyone has heard of mystery calls. It's a very popular concept that has crept into dentistry. But there is a significant liability with using an outside service to perform mystery calls. Very often, you have sales training companies representing themselves as training companies that offer to conduct a mystery call on your office. The problems begin with the call. They are very skilled at ensuring that every call fails so that they can sell you an expensive sales program. They almost invariably blame the team member. It's very divisive, and creates a lot of tension between the staff and doctor. You don't want that. You want to do something that's ethical that identifies skill gaps and areas that need improvement – all presented in a constructive manner that emphasizes a path to improvement.

One way to ethically evaluate calls is to conduct them yourself, or have someone you are familiar with place the call. Even better, though, is to take a listen to real calls with real patients, who are asking real questions. The technology to easily record calls is commonplace. The staff does not have to be afraid of real calls, and they can't argue with reality. One key is that you need an effective grading system that reflects your principles – one that is based on building rapport with callers, versus simply "getting 'em in" for an appointment. The team's enthusiasm and confidence increase when they hear themselves on the phone and are graded in a constructive manner rather than being put down.

There are a couple call recording options if you're not doing this already. One option is to get a tracking number on a website. The associated call services are as cheap as half a cent per minute. You can also use a service that does call recording and then provides detailed statistics. You'll get feedback on who's handling the calls, how many new patients were scheduled, how many existing patients were scheduled Or, if you have a Voice over Internet (VOIP) system, check to see if calls can be automatically recorded. Basically, record your phone calls. It's very affordable to do, and it's a powerful learning tool to listen to live, real phone calls. One caveat is that you need to make sure that you record calls in such a way as to remain HIPAA compliant.

What about role playing? If you are unfamiliar with the concept, role playing is a practical way to exercise new skills learned in a training program. How do you do a role play? It's easy!

Choose a scenario with common issues, such as regularly asked questions or objections that your staff routinely faces, such as office is too far, what's the price for _____, do you take my insurance... etc. You assign roles to two team members - who's going to be a patient, who's going to be reception. Have them sit back-to-back to make it a bit more realistic - remember there is no eye contact over the phone! Have a third person grade the role play call and provide instant, positive and constructive feedback.

Training Habits

Is training ever done? I've heard team members say, "You know what? I'm finishing training, I'm done! I know it!" But, really, they probably just *think* they are done. True professionals are always striving to improve their skills. Think about great athletes, such as Michael Jordan. Whether you like him or not, you should know that aside from his natural talent, he was one of the hardest working basketball players out there. He practiced and practiced and practiced. The way your staff trains will be reflected in how they perform on calls. So if they work hard, care about the process and results, study, practice, listen to calls, apply what they have learned, you're going to end up with the best dental team in the business.

According to a study by Brian Tracy International, it takes four units of energy to start a project but only one unit of energy to keep it going. This is a problem that many dental practices experience when training only once a year. It takes extra money, time, and energy to start and stop, versus starting and maintaining as a regular activity.

Related to this is what is called the "training effect." I saw the training effect in action during my time as a Tony Robbins consultant. A team does some training, and there is an improvement in skill. Naturally, much of the improvement in skills is lost after training ends, but certain skills "stick" and become permanent. This effect cycles as we train and improve skills, then diminish after training ends, with some new or improved skills becoming permanent. It's very common for offices to start training, get really excited, and improve. Unfortunately, though, the typical behavior is to then take a break from training. At that point, most of the improvements are lost.

Training Effect

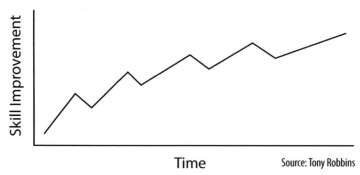

Skill Improvement

Time

Source: Tony Robbins

Consistent training results in a general trend of overall improvement over time, with less diminishing of skills because you are not stopping. If you stick with it, you're going to see ultimate growth and improvement and sustain those improvements.

So the key to success is on-going, comprehensive training. Get new team members onboard quickly and then transition to comprehensive training. Build it into the culture of your business. Short training sessions (20 minutes a week!) with review in meetings, role playing, and call evaluations. You'll have your team on track to stardom!

There is one other concept I want to talk about that may seal the deal, and that's called modeling. You want to do what the best in dentistry are doing, so you can mimic their success.

So what are the best dentists doing? Well, they're committed to patient service, they have a business that works for them, they hire the best team members, they invest in training not just for themselves but for their team, and they're open-minded and humble.

And what about the best team members? They're committed to patient service, they have initiative, they love learning, and they love feedback. They don't know it all.

The most obvious benefits of training?

First, you're going to have reduced turnover, which the costs associated with replacing an employee. I showed you how keeping a good employee will save you $30,000 in turnover expenses. In other words, the math shows that *the cost of training is far less than the cost to replace an employee.* This is even before the benefit of improved conversion and reduced broken appointments.

According to the American Society for Training and Development your revenue per employee goes up by 218% when you invest in training. That's huge! And according to a study conducted by Accenture a $600 investment in training per employee will net you a 6% higher take home.

The second benefit that comes from training is an improvement in morale and confidence. An ILX Group Study shows that training improves employee morale by 51%. You're going to have higher job satisfaction, better organizational commitment, and better performance. And the number one stressor for YOU is reduced. You will simply have less stress from happier employees.

In a recent webinar, we had a question asked: How much should a dentist invest in ongoing training per year with respect to customer service and practice management? Is there a % or $ amount?

Allen M. Schiff, CPA, CFE, and President of the Academy of Dental CPAs, suggests, "Practices should look at the practice management fees not as *fees*, but as **an investment!** My suggestion is that the dollar investment (depending on the size of the practice, along with the growth you are looking to obtain) should range between $1,500 to $2,500 a month for at least the first 18 months of engagement, and then consider 'maintenance' fee after the initial investment."

It's a valuable perspective on how to approach the dollars you put toward training.

Here's some feedback we got from Mindy, a patient coordinator who is using our program, on how the training program helped her. "I'm new to dentistry, but worked in the medical field for the past nine years. My new dentist provided me a very helpful tool, All-Star Dental Academy. The courses have been very helpful as well as motivating. One of the things that I find to be most difficult is communicating over the phone with patients in regards to scheduling and insurance questions. The GREAT Call™ Process has been amazing in helping me find the right verbiage and improving my confidence in dealing with these calls. I look forward to continuing the program and becoming more successful with the help of All-Star Dental Academy."

And I spoke with her doctor, Dr. Todd Synder, a top cosmetic dentist, and he said, "You know, this has just been amazing for me. My whole team is doing this, my hygienist, everybody. I say 'You do your program, you go at your own pace. We'll talk about it.' I don't have to worry about it. I don't have to be stressed. I know they're being trained. I can focus on dentistry and I can go home at the end of the day knowing that they're trained. I don't have to bother with it and I'm happy."

Sounds good to me!

CHAPTER 6

NO MORE EXCUSES

Chapter 6: NO MORE EXCUSES

We have talked at length about external forces that influence how you run your business: insurance companies, corporate dentistry, marketing saturation, patient buying power, and competition. You should realize, though, there are other issues that can prevent you from achieving success, even before you begin to consider external forces. The absolute nemesis of the appropriate mindset for success is an excuse.

Here are some of the most common, right from the dentists we polled and asked WHY they don't train:

"I want to wait to train until I have the right people."

Would you rather have less than ideal staff remain UNTRAINED, or the less than ideal staff that IS trained? The answer should be obvious. The reality is it will take a while to find new employees so while you're looking, train who you have. Get a return from every ounce of investment you put into them. Convert more calls, and get rid of those broken appointments. If you feel like you have the wrong people, train them anyway. Train them until you find the right people.

"I've trained in the past, but it's hard to get started and keep momentum. I just know my team won't have time."

The first question to ask yourself is do you have 20 minutes a week? Of course you do. So, really, it is an issue of leadership. You are the boss. You say, "Do it. Do it and I'm going to check on you at the end of the week and see how it's going. We'll talk about it for a few minutes." That's it. Successful businesspeople, including dentists, do what others don't want to do. This is about getting things done and making real change. There's no quick fix. You have to step up and do it.

"My team is already 'pretty good' on the phone."

Are you satisfied with being a "pretty good" dentist? The problem with a "pretty good" team is that is exactly the impression they will give to your patients - that you are only "pretty good." The best are always striving to improve, and to improve you need to train consistently and often. The very best always revisit the basics. They maintain a beginners mindset.

"I've spent a ton of money on consulting and training. I didn't make money, in fact, I actually lost money. So I don't want to waste more money."

It is unfortunate that there are so many companies out there working hard to separate you from your money. But, look at the end result of not training. Poor conversion, tons of broken appointments, poor patient experience, poor referrals. But, ask yourself some hard questions. Perhaps previous challenges with training were your fault. Maybe you didn't listen to the consultant. It could be that you didn't provide good leadership to your team.

So my recommendation is do your research, make sure the training company or consultant you want to bring in aligns with your business philosophies. Start small, and build little by little. You don't have to go, "Boom, we're going to change this, that, that, change that. By next month!" Instead, aim for incremental improvements, a little bit every week. In the end, it will all add up and make a big difference.

"We're too busy."

Over 15% of those dentists we polled said "We're too busy to train." And typically they're too busy because they're not training, they're not efficient. They're unproductively busy. Wouldn't you rather take some of that time and invest in training so you can be less busy? You just have to spend the time. I think some people assume, "Oh, training has to take hours!" I understand the assumption, but no, 20 minutes a week. That's it. That's a few dollars per employee of their time. No big deal.

"My staff isn't interested."

Nearly 25% of those dentists polled said that they expected a lot of resistance to training from their staff. There are some different elements that contribute to this attitude: if you're going to give your staff a program that's going to teach borderline unethical sales schemes, they're going to push back, and I hope they do. That resistance shows your team has good moral character. Or maybe the program is boring, or it's too difficult and complicated. But, if it's a good program and they're not training, they're being stubborn and probably thinking, "I don't want to train. I know it already." That's a big problem. First, you are the boss, and they need to do what is required of them. But if you still get resistance, then you'll need to start looking elsewhere for people who have the right mindset. Find someone who's motivated and wants to make a difference.

"Training is too expensive."

Another 25% say, "Training is too expensive." That's understandable because most training takes place in seminars, or you'll bring in a consultant, or buy some program where they are constantly trying to upsell you to a more profitable product. We love seminars and consultants, but they are most valuable when you and the team are ready for some specific work. But, you seriously need to consider, as we've talked about, the real costs of NOT training. Spend a bit to train your staff, or wave good-bye to potentially hundreds of thousands in additional revenue.

"There's no quality training out there."

Finally, and this surprised me, 35% said, "I can't find a quality program that I like." This is precisely why we created All-Star Dental Academy, dentistry's most comprehensive online phone skills and productive scheduling training program. It's designed to get results in 30 to 90 days and instill a long-term competitive advantage through teaching a service-based approach to the patient experience. And we do it by empowering your staff, not tearing them down.

So to review, you have your external forces: insurance companies, corporate dentistry, marketing saturation, patient buying power, and competition. They will "eat you for lunch," UNLESS you balance them by investing energy in developing your team to the point where you can provide customer-winning service. You have to train like the Fortune 500: onboarding and comprehensive training. Your focus needs to be converting phone calls to patients using amazing customer service and the GREAT Call™ Process, banishing broken appointments, and developing and keeping great team members to avoid costly turnover and mistakes. Really, our whole goal is to help you develop self-determination. To give you the freedom that comes from working for yourself – you can do whatever you want to do, however you want to live your life.

CHAPTER 7

FAST TRACK TO SUCCESS

Chapter 7: FAST TRACK TO SUCCESS

This last chapter is all about action. I'm going to give you a bit more fuel, and then what you need to blast off.

Let's take a look at the big picture. Every day you are bleeding money from the symptoms of the silent killer. Do the math. To be conservative, we'll just evaluate the short-term costs.

Start with 16 missed call opportunities per month, only one per working day, at $642 (ADA's first visit value). Adds up to $10,000 in missed call opportunities per month.

Remember, ONE missed opportunity is extremely conservative. What about broken appointments? Two broken appointments per week for the doctor, at $500 an hour, is $4,000 a month. Eight times in hygiene per week, at $100 an hour, is $3,200 per month.

What about the costs associated with turnover? One employee lost per year, 100% cost of their entry-level salary at $30,000 is $30,000.

Well let's add them up.

Call conversion: **$10,000 a month,**

Broken appointments: **$7,200 a month,**

Turnover: **$2,500 a month** ($30,000 divided by 12), gives you **nearly $20,000 in revenue bleeding out per month.**

In this analysis, we're using 16 working days per month, and if you divide $20,000 a month by 16, you are **losing $1,250** per day only on call conversion opportunities, broken appointments, and turnover.

We have worked with practices that were missing many more calls per day, and broken appointments happening all the time. We have even seen practices where entire teams turn over in a year, like a revolving door. Many practices are in much worse situations than what we are describing here, but let's just be conservative and use this case of $1,250 a day for the average practice.

How can you put a stop to this bleeding?

The solution is All-Star Dental Academy®.

With All-Star's training program, you're getting solutions to all the challenges outlined in this book.

You'll get an onboarding program, on-going, comprehensive training, an exhaustive look at the GREAT Call™ Process, learn more specific techniques and verbiage to banish broken appointments, and insight into the Triple "S" Scheduling System which will teach you and your team how to schedule patients for maximum productivity. All of this is online/on-demand 24/7, and is presented in bite-sized video lectures.

You should know that we have limited seats in our program. We do this because we want to provide the highest level of service to those dentists that are ready to make a difference in their practice immediately. It's first come first served. If you're serious about beginning All-Star Dental Academy® I encourage to get in touch with us ASAP otherwise you're going to wind up on a waiting list.

Part of the reason enrollment closes so quickly is because we work with some amazing organizations that promote All-Star to their members. I've mentioned that the AACD (American Academy of Cosmetic Dentistry) is one of our partners and we provide member benefits for the AGD (Academy of General Dentistry). Recently, the AACD said this about our relationship: "We partnered with All-Star Dental Academy® because they share our commitment to quality and service when providing top-notch training in phone conversion and productive scheduling for dental teams."

So sign up now. At the end of the book, you'll find instructions on where to visit so you can sign up for All-Star Dental Academy® and begin training immediately.

All-Star Dental Academy® Training Program Tour

I mentioned some of the features of the Training Program, but I want to take some time to give you a more involved look around.

You and your team will start with QuickStart, our onboarding component. QuickStart teaches the fundamentals of phone verbiage and productive scheduling to get your team more effective, fast. Recall that all of our training programs are broken down into bite-sized units of five to fifteen minutes. The length makes them perfect for individual training, a team meeting or even a huddle. QuickStart is designed to get results in 30 to 90 days.

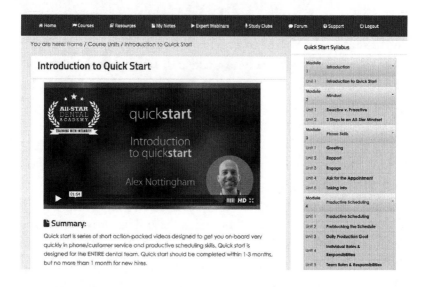

Introduction to Quick Start

quick**start**

Introduction
to quick**start**

Alex Nottingham

01:54 |||| HD ::

Quick Start Syllabus

Module 1	Introduction
Unit 1	Introduction to Quick Start
Module 2	Mindset
Unit 1	Reactive v. Proactive
Unit 2	3 Steps to an All-Star Mindset
Module 3	Phone Skills
Unit 1	Greeting
Unit 2	Rapport
Unit 3	Engage
Unit 4	Ask for the Appointment
Unit 5	Taking Info
Module 4	Productive Scheduling
Unit 1	Productive Scheduling
Unit 2	Preblocking the Schedule
Unit 3	Daily Production Goal
Unit 4	Individual Roles & Responsibilities
Unit 5	Team Roles & Responsibilities

📄 Summary:

Quick start is series of short action-packed videos designed to get you on-board very quickly in phone/customer service and productive scheduling skills. Quick start is designed for the ENTIRE dental team. Quick start should be completed within 1-3 months, but no more than 1 month for new hires.

You and your team will move on to the most comprehensive phone and scheduling training program on the market: Phone Success and Scheduling Advantage. Again, all you need to do is invest 20 minutes per week and you're going to be in great shape for the rest of the year, don't rush through it. Do little by little, stick with it, and you'll be amazed with the results that you get.

Here are just a few topics we cover in our comprehensive courses:

- Patient communication and psychology
- Rapport building
- Overcoming objections
- Handling price shoppers and the insurance question
- 20+ role play transcripts with video instruction
- Verbiage for the whole team
- The GREAT Call™ Process
- Productive scheduling
- Reduce or eliminate broken appointments
- Reactivation of patients
- Pre-blocking

- Scheduling verbiage
- Production goals
- Advanced scheduling techniques
- And much more!

Once you sign up and log in, you and your team will have access to the step-by-step Action Plans that take you through the program to get you up to speed quickly, and lay out a training plan that facilitates continuous success. All-Star is designed to be a consistent aid to growth for years to come.

Each course in the program is accompanied by a Study Guide that will help you stay focused, take notes, and retain concepts. Also you're going to get 20+ role plays and transcripts much like the one we shared with you earlier. We have included quizzes in the courses, and an exam at the end of each course to help track progress and give feedback.

All of our courses have the opportunity for continuing education credits. We are AGD PACE accredited and the relevant information will be provided upon successful completion of a certification exam.

We are always working to keep our courses up to date and adding more resources to help your practice succeed.

Plus, we just released All-Star Dental Academy® 3.0, which includes a multiple user platform. So, each team member gets their own login, and you can monitor their progress and quiz results. Every account has ten users, but if you need additional users they can be added at a reduced rate.

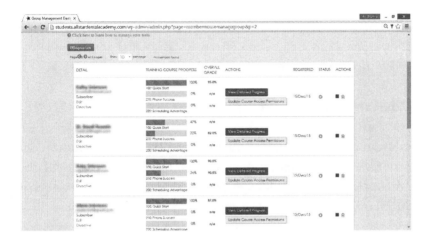

No Risk

Now here's what makes All-Star's training program a no-brainer: there's no risk. If after the first year of training with us, you don't see a 10 times improvement in value, we will pay for your second, third, whatever years to come of All-Star Dental Academy® until you reach 10 times your initial investment. This is our 10X Performance Guarantee.

And the reality is, you are likely losing upwards of $1,250 every day. To end that, you're going to have to train. And that's even before the challenges posed by those external forces: insurance companies, corporate dentistry, marketing saturation, patient buying power, and competition.

Hopefully you'll agree that the solution to these challenges is to train your team to provide effective call conversion, productive scheduling and superior customer service.

What are your alternatives?

You can go to a weekend seminar that will run you around $7,500 for travel, and expenses, and your employees' tuition. And the amount of content you'll receive is not even close to what you get at All-Star Dental Academy®. It's also not presented in the most effective way to learn and retain. Like I said earlier, when you get back to work, what's going to happen? Chances are absolutely nothing will come from it.

You can hire a consultant. I'm sure you've thought about it before, but were put off by the cost. Top consultants will charge you as much as $100,000. They may be effective, but will your team put it into action? And do consultants have any kind of guarantee?

Finally, you can try to do it the hard way – all on your own. The problem with this is that you should really be doing what you do best – dentistry, and leave the training to those who specialize in it. And while you are learning it on your own, you are most likely still losing that $20,000 a month (or even scarier, look at that annually - $240,000 a year!).

I want to share some kind words from our students.

Dr. Chris Jaghab said this about our program, "If you plan on doing bigger cases... All-Star Dental Academy® is the only program of its kind. They teach a patient-centered, customer service oriented system based on authentic, effective communication. I have never found a program like it. Their support is outstanding and they're always adding additional, relevant content from the industry's leading practice management experts. If you plan to have an all-star dental practice, then you need All-Star Dental Academy®."

Dr. Jaghab's team was begging for All-Star's training program, so he signed up. A week later he sent me an email and said, "Wow, I'm already seeing results!"

Dr. Linda Winter said, "We're loving being students of the All-Star Dental Academy®. The exercises are short enough that we don't lose our focus. As a team we're working on critiquing each other as we now have a common basis for looking at our practice. I highly recommend this to anyone who wants to improve their customer service and call conversion."

I'm not done yet...

By now you're probably thinking, "I need All-Star's training program for my practice." But I put together something that makes signing up even easier. I'm going to make available three bonuses to get you started on All-Star Dental Academy®. These bonuses alone are valued at more than tuition to the training program.

I call the first bonus piece the Content Booster. You're going to get a resource library of systems, materials, forms, and educational processes. And you're going to have access to our monthly Expert Webinars where we interview a leading expert in dentistry and come away with actionable knowledge that will have an impact on your practice. You'll have access to a library of past Expert Webinars – replays that you can review at any time. We've interviewed experts like Debra Nash, Dr. Lorne Lavine, Dr. Joseph Michelli the New York Times bestselling customer service authority. He wrote about how Starbucks and The Ritz Carlton have made customer service part of their culture and a competitive advantage. The Content Booster alone is valued at $2,500 a year.

You'll also get access to our Virtual Mastermind. Each month you'll have the opportunity to interact with All-Star Dental Academy® instructors in our Study Club. We go into detail on a number of timely issues. In past events, we talked about how to get more fee-for-service clients, working with insurance, how to banish broken appointments, and eliminating drama in the office. Everyone attending is able to ask questions and interact with members of the team. We can also address off topic questions about, really, anything. Another part of the Virtual Mastermind is the Expert Forum. Ask questions and get answers from a variety of people from the industry (All-Star instructors, consultants, speakers, and other dentists). We've valued the Virtual Mastermind at $2,000 a year.

All-Star Dental Academy® has been designed as a self-study program. You never need to go to another seminar or hire another consultant ever again.

That said, consultants and seminars are fantastic! We have many industry experts that are certified to coach or train clients using our material.

Many of our dental offices ask "How can I turbo charge my All-Star experience. How can I get there faster?"

The answer is simple. *Work with a coach.*

As a former top consultant and coach for Tony Robbins, I got to see first hand the power of coaching. Look around. All the top athletes and business executives have coaches.

Did you know?

- Research by BBI International showed that 75% of Fortune 500 CEO's state coaching as one of their top three factors of success
- A study by Fortune Magazine found that a: "...conservative estimate of monetary payoff from coaching... returns SIX TIMES what the coaching cost their companies."
- Coaching brings specialized knowledge to your business, a unique perspective, and helps to spot "gaps" that you may not be seeing

We recommend that if you are interested in coaching that you look for a "self-funding" coach. What this means is that any investment in a coach pays off well beyond the cost, much like the Fortune Magazine study suggests. All of our All-Star Dental Academy® coaches are self-funding coaches.

We have wonderful coaches that are certified in our process and philosophy. They are vetted as real trainers, that have all worked successfully in dentistry. They are NOT sales-people.

Only All-Star certified coaches are permitted to implement the All-Star program because they have been through a rigorous certification process and have mastered how to implement the program effectively.

So, for my last bonus, you're going to get our Accountability Suite. You're going to get a training program power call with an All-Star Dental Academy® Mastery Coach. We want to help you get started and pointed in the right direction.

You also get call evaluation and grading. Send us one call a month and we will provide constructive and objective feedback on your progress. You email us, provide access to a recorded call, and we will grade it using our GREAT Call™ Process. The Accountability Suite is valued at $2,000 a year.

Add up the Content Booster, the Virtual Mastermind, and the Accountability Suite, and you're looking at $6,500 in additional value. We are packaging them altogether to make signing up for All-Star's training program a total no-brainer.

All You Will Ever Need...

Here are some more positive words from our students:

Victor P., office manager, says, "We have tried seminars and consulting firms in the past, but really did not get the meat of the skills needed. We signed on to All-Star Dental Academy® and got the team onboard after phone meeting with an All-Star coach. After six months, all of our front office team, including new members, are certified. We use the training materials all day, every day, and I am very happy with the professionalism our business team members demonstrate."

All-Star Dental Academy® is the only training program you will ever need. With All-Star you ensure a baseline of solid training. You can certainly go to seminars, invest in coaching and consulting, but now you know you haven't missed anything. All your bases are covered. You will not find anything on the market like this for this price, not even close. This is why we book up so quickly.

Dr. Lorne Lavine, The Digital Dentist, said this: "All-Star Dental Academy® is doing great things. They are helping practices focus on customer service and how to schedule more effectively. Every practice should have All-Star Dental Academy® training alongside their practice management software." Dr. Lavine believes so much in All-Star that he joined as an instructor.

Rachel Wall from Inspired Hygiene said, "All-Star Dental Academy® makes learning easy. They have wonderful resources, instructors, of which I'm one, and most importantly they are great people. Thank you All-Star Dental Academy® for your leadership."

Marilee Sears of Future of Dentistry said "All-Star Dental Academy® is the best, most thorough, comprehensive training for scheduling and phone skills that I've seen!"

Go ahead and sign up for All-Star Dental Academy® by visiting allstardentalacademy.com or call Heather at 954.323.2220. You're going to get the QuickStart which is the onboarding training program. You're going to get the most comprehensive phone and scheduling training program on the market, a 10X performance guarantee, the resource library, the Expert Webinars, Study Clubs, Expert Forum, Mastery Coach, Call Grading… over $9,500 in yearly value.

For those who have been diligent and read all the way here, I have a few gifts to send your way. The first gift is a very powerful cheat sheet on questions to ask during a call to build rapport and uncover patient needs. This is going to help you with that rapport building process. This comes right out of our resource library, and is one of the many documents that we provide as part of the training program.

The second gift is from a Study Club event where talked about broken appointments. We talk in great detail about broken appointments in our Scheduling Advantage course, but the topic is so important that we address it in our Expert Webinars and in Study Club sessions. We go into greater detail and reiterate important points. I'm going to give you the entire Study Club transcript. If you would like the audio to listen to let us know and I'll get you that as well.

The third gift is a free call evaluation and grading. You email us and provide access to a recorded call, and we will grade using our

GREAT Call™ Process. So you'll get some constructive and objective feedback on a real, live call. The first two bonuses were content-specific, while the third is going to help you with implementation. Email Heather at heather@allstardentalacademy.com, provide your name, practice name, and your website (so we can learn a little bit more about you), and she will get you all set up.

And I have one last thing for all of you troopers staying through to the end of this book. If you sign up for All-Star Dental Academy® and mention that you have read this book, you will get a strategy call with me - an additional $500 value. What is the strategy call? We're going to meet and I'm going to learn about your office, get an understanding of your unique challenges, and then make specific recommendations on how to best implement the training program and move forward.

One other thing... we understand that a struggling practice, new graduates, or associates may find it difficult to find the extra cash to start with All-Star, so in those cases, we can work with you to get your team training. Email Heather@allstardentalacademy.com.

Thank you for making an investment of your time in reading this book! We look forward to helping you unlock your practice's true potential for success.